The Wizard's Book of Science Secrets

HI ZINC
ISLAND SCIENCE
PARTNERSHIP

&

WIZARD IV

© 2011 HiZinc, LLC

ISBN 978-0-983606-60-4

Design and production
Lawrence Art & Design Studios
Lead design: Donavan Lawrence

Illustrations
Donavan Lawrence
iStock.com

HiZinc, LLC
333 Kilauea Avenue, Suite 214
Hilo, Hawaii 96720

10 9 8 7 6 5 4 3 2

Printed in Korea

A Message from Wizard IV

To be a science wizard, you don't need a laboratory filled with fancy equipment. Many of the world's most famous scientists made great discoveries and inventions using common, everyday items.

Michael Faraday (Wizard I) used sealing wax and thread to make insulation for the world's first electromagnet. Guglielmo Marconi used baling wire and strips cut from tin cans as parts for his early radio transmitters. Alexander Graham Bell used thread spools to wind coils for his early telephones. Marie Curie used hammers, kitchen pans and large soup ladles while processing minerals in her quest for Radium.

A great place to find a good inventory of scientific equipment and supplies is as close as your neighborhood hardware store. Each department in the store contains items that you can use to perform many scientific tricks, experiments and demonstrations.

The pages of this "Wizard's Notebook" will not only show you how to transform everyday items into scientific apparatus, but will also teach you how to "think like a scientist." While building and performing activities in this book, you'll be encouraged to repeat those process skills used by scientists around the world. You'll practice making observations, taking careful measurements, making predictions, solving problems and keeping records.

Scientist are experts at "trying it again"! If your trick or experiment doesn't work the first time, don't give up. You might need to make only slight adjustments to your equipment.

Scientists are also safety experts. Practice being careful when handling equipment or materials that are sharp or generate heat or flame. A scientist always seeks help from others, so don't be afraid to ask an adult for help at any time.

Perhaps, while searching the aisles of the store for an addition to your hardware laboratory, you might find just the right piece of hardware for your very own scientific discovery or invention. A trip to the hardware store can get you started on many fantastic scientific adventures. In just a short time you might be mysteriously floating a screwdriver in mid-air, or scooting across your driveway on a homemade hovercraft!

# ⚠ Safety ⚠

Follow these safety rules when performing activities in this book:

1. Wear eye protection when doing a science activity.

2. Learn how to safely dispose of all materials used in the activity.

3. Keep a fire extinguisher and first aid kit handy, and know how to use them.

4. Wear appropriate clothing when performing any activity. Avoid wearing loose or bulky clothing.

5. Understand all elements of the activity before performing it. Ask questions if you do not understand.

6. Use only the size of equipment and quantities of materials suggested in the directions.

7. Make certain all people and property in the area of your science activity are well protected and informed.

"The wizards are a strange class of kindly
mortal, impelled by an almost insane impulse to
seek their pleasure among smoke and vapor, soot
and flame, poisons and poverty. Yet among all
these evils they seem to live so sweetly that
they may die if they would change places with
even a King."

Johann Joachim Becher, phlogistonist   1669

Contents

All of these activities came from the collections of four Wizards. Some were presented over 200 years ago. Over the centuries they have inspired millions of young wizards and scientists to enjoy the process of scientific thought while learning and having fun.

CATCH A FALLING STAR

What is it? Using a magnet and plastic bucket, you can collect micro-meteorites that have fallen on your roof!

What you'll need:
Checklist:
☐ Small, strong magnet
☐ Plastic bucket

Optional:
☐ Magnifier
☐ Garden hose
☐ Small metal file

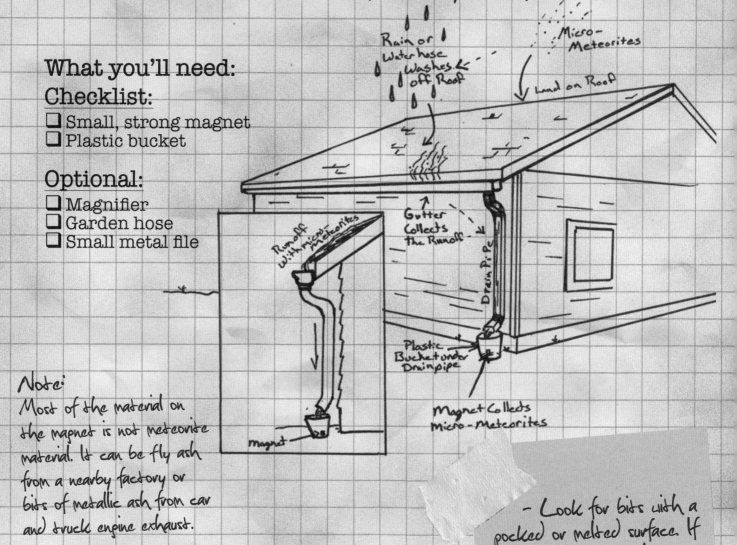

Rain or Water hose Washes off Roof

Micro-Meteorites

Land on Roof

Gutter Collects the Runoff

Runoff with micro-meteorites

Drain Pipe

Plastic Bucket under Drainpipe

magnet

Magnet Collects micro-meteorites

Note:
Most of the material on the magnet is not meteorite material. It can be fly ash from a nearby factory or bits of metallic ash from car and truck engine exhaust.

- Look for bits with a pocked or melted surface. If they are large enough, use a file to remove a bit of the surface coating to expose the shiny nickel-iron metal content in the meteorite.

Here's How:
1. Place the magnet in the bottom of a bucket.
2. Place the bucket under a gutter downspout.
3. Wait for a rain shower, or wash off your roof with a garden hose.
4. Inspect the magnet. It will be covered with small specks of materials...some are micro-meteorites!

The Science:

Over 200 million meteors enter the earth's atmosphere each day. Most meteors are the size of grains of sand and burn up in the atmosphere. Enough of them fall to the earth to add about 1000 tons of mass to the earth every day.

Meteors that reach the earth's surface are called meteorites. There are two main types of meteorites: stony and iron-nickel. The iron-nickel variety is attracted to magnets.

The best time to observe meteors large enough to create the shooting star effect is after midnight. One should be able to observe an average of one meteor every ten minutes. The count will be much higher during a meteor shower.

Sketches & Observations:

Notes:

_____
_____
_____
_____
_____
_____
_____
_____
_____
_____
_____
_____
_____
_____

Copper Wire Heat Sink

What is it? A candle flame is magically extinguished using nothing other than a piece of copper wire.

What you'll need:
Checklist:
- ☐ A candle
- ☐ Matches
- ☐ Bare copper wire, 22 to 28 gauge
- ☐ A sharpened pencil

Important Notes:
-Make certain you use wire that has NO insulation.
-Protect surfaces from dripping candle wax.
-Don't burn your fingers!

Here's How:
1. Form a cone-shaped coil of wire by wrapping the wire around the end of a sharpened pencil.
2. Create a wire "handle" by leaving several inches of wire uncoiled.
3. Spread the wraps of coil wire apart, leaving a gap between each wrap.
4. Safely light a candle.
5. Slowly lower the wire cone into the flame. The flame will be extinguished...without blowing on it or smothering it!

The Science:

Fuel, heat and oxygen are required for a common flame to exist. This device does not remove the fuel or the oxygen/air.

Copper is an excellent conductor of heat energy. In this activity, the copper wire conducts heat away from the flame so rapidly that the chemical reaction stops.

Good heat conductors like copper and other metals are often used to remove heat from machinery or chemical reactions.

- How many times can you conduct this activity before the copper wire is full of heat and no longer puts out the flame?

Sketches & Observations:

Notes:

_____
_____
_____
_____
_____
_____
_____
_____
_____
_____
_____
_____
_____

TAPE THERMOMETER

What is it? A sensitive heat-detecting device can be made from two pieces of tape!

What you'll need:
Checklist:
- ☐ Wide masking tape
- ☐ Wide cellophane or transparent tape
- ☐ Electric lamp

Don't touch the bulb!

Here's How:
1. Cut a six-inch strip of both tapes.
2. Stick the tape strips together, sticky side to sticky side.
3. Turn on the lamp and allow the bulb to warm up.
4. Hold one end of the strip over the warm bulb.
5. Notice how the strip curls when it warms up... and how it uncurls as it cools.

The Science:

Many common materials expand when they are heated...and contract when they cool.

However, different materials often expand at different rates.

Observe the tape strip as it curls. Can you determine which tape is expanding more than the other as they are heated?

How sensitive is your thermometer? Can it detect slight temperature changes?

Some thermostats (the device on a wall that turns the furnace on and off) use a bi-metal strip similar to the tape thermometer.

Sketches & Observations:

Notes:

_____
_____
_____
_____
_____
_____
_____
_____
_____
_____
_____
_____
_____
_____

STEEL WOOL OXYGEN DETECTOR

What is it? You can use a jar and some steel wool to observe a common chemical reaction take place. Over several days, water will mysteriously rise in the jar.

What you'll need:
Checklist:
☐ Fine steel wool
☐ Glass or plastic jar
☐ Pan or bowl
☐ Water
☐ Wax pencil or marker

-Be careful handling the steel wool. It can make small cuts in your skin.

-If nothing happens after several days, try rinsing new steel wool to remove oil or grease on the steel fibers.

Water Height

Here's How:

1. Rinse a small handful of fine steel wool with warm tap water. Rinse the steel wool several times.

2. Firmly pack the damp steel wool into the bottom of the jar.

3. Fill a small bowl of water with tap water.

4. Fill the jar about 1/2 full with water.

5. Invert the jar (upside down) in the bowl of water.

6. Use a marker to indicate the level of water in the jar. You may need to adjust the amount of water you put in the jar.

7. Each day, place another mark on the water level in the jar.

The Science:

What we commonly call "rust" is actually a chemical compound called iron oxide. Oxygen in our air reacts with many materials...including iron. That is why materials made with iron must be coated with oil or paint to prevent the oxidation reaction from taking place.

In your jar, as oxygen in the air reacts with the steel wool (steel is made from iron), the volume of air decreases, allowing water to rise in the jar. Air pressure on the outside of the jar pushes down on the water in the bowl, causing it to rise inside the jar.

Sketches & Observations:

Notes:

_____
_____
_____
_____
_____
_____
_____
_____
_____
_____
_____
_____
_____

CENTER OF GRAVITY TRICK

What is it? A real head-scratcher, this is a classic gravity-defying science magic trick that looks impossible!

What you'll need:
Checklist:
- ☐ A drinking glass or tumbler (glass – not plastic!)
- ☐ A metal fork with four tines
- ☐ A metal spoon
- ☐ Wood matchsticks, or similar-sized wood splint

This takes a bit of practice – don't use plastic!

You may have to try different forks to find one that makes a snug fit with the matchstick.

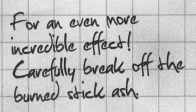

– For an extra bit of excitement light the end of the match that is inside the glass rim

For an even more incredible effect! Carefully break off the burned stick ash.

Here's How:
1. Push the spoon bowl between the fork tines as shown.
2. Insert a large wood matchstick into the outermost pair of tines.
3. Swivel the matchstick back and forth until you locate a position that lets it balance on your finger.
4. Use that point to balance the matchstick on the rim of the glass.

The Science:

The center of gravity, often called the balance point, is defined as the point at which the entire weight of an object may be considered to act. The center of gravity is not always on the interior of an object.

In the case of a solid steel ball bearing, which is of uniform shape and density, the center of gravity is at the very center of the sphere. In the case of a boomerang, the center of gravity is located outside the object, between the two arms.

The center of gravity of the strangely shaped object created with the fork and spoon is not within the object. When you adjust the position of the match by pulling in and out, or side to side, you are attempting to locate that center of gravity. Once the match is positioned over the center of gravity, the system can be balanced easily.

When the match is lit inside the glass rim, it burns until the flames reach the glass. The glass conducts away sufficient heat, cooling the flame below combustion temperature...and the flame goes out!

Sketches & Observations:

Notes:

Longer than Tall

What is it? Make yourself two inches taller...or two inches shorter! Not really. But you can measure how the length of your body dramatically changes when you alter positions.

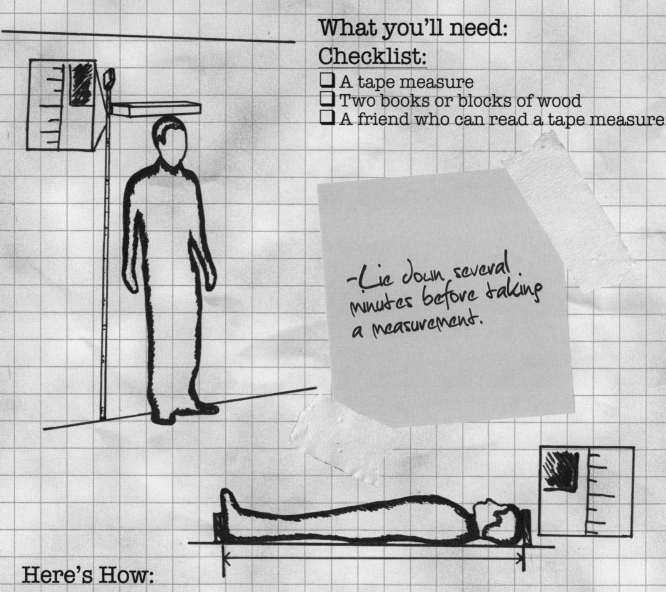

What you'll need:
Checklist:
- ☐ A tape measure
- ☐ Two books or blocks of wood
- ☐ A friend who can read a tape measure

- Lie down several minutes before taking a measurement.

Here's How:
1. Recline on the floor or other firm surface.
2. Place the top of your head against the wall or hard surface.
3. Have your assistant place a book or board at the bottom of your feet.
4. Using the tape, measure your length.
5. Stand against the wall and measure your height.
6. Make note of the difference in measurements.

The Science:

When we stand up, gravity compresses the space between our bones, making us a bit shorter. When we lie down, we compress in a different direction due to gravity. The length of our body expands a bit...one to two inches, on average.

Sketches & Observations:

Notes:

_____
_____
_____
_____
_____
_____
_____
_____
_____
_____
_____
_____

LIGHT FROM A LIFESAVER

What is it? You can make lightning in your mouth, using only mint candy.

What you'll need:
Checklist:
☐ Wint-O-Green Life Savers™
  (or similar)

Optional:
☐ Pliers
☐ Small mirror

Note:
-Moisture in the mouth may hinder the effect.

-As an alternative, the wintergreen mints can be crushed with pliers.

Here's How:
1. This activity must be performed in a very dark room.
2. Some wintergreen candy brands other than Lifesavers™ also work for this activity.
3. Clear your mouth of as much saliva as possible.
4. While keeping your lips apart, crunch the candy in your mouth.
5. Small flashes of blue light are emitted.

The Science:

Ingredients combined to make wintergreen mints form a crystal that breaks in flat sheets. Often, one side of the break will contain more electrons than the other. A pulse of invisible ultraviolet light is generated as the excess electrons jump back. That UV pulse excites molecules in the mint sufficiently to emit a pulse of visible light.

Sketches & Observations:

Notes:

_____
_____
_____
_____
_____
_____
_____
_____
_____
_____
_____
_____
_____
_____

SIMPLE ELECTRIC MOTOR

What is it? Using a few small items and a flashlight cell, you can build an operating electric motor.

What you'll need:
Checklist:
- ☐ D flashlight battery
- ☐ Rubber bands
- ☐ Needle-nose pliers
- ☐ Fine sandpaper or emery nail file
- ☐ Broom handle
- ☐ Four feet of this copper wire*
- ☐ Magnet*
- ☐ Small sticks

Optional:
- ☐ Glue

- *Use wire that does not have thick plastic insulation. Use varnished or lacquered copper wire. 22- to 28-gauge wire works well.
- *The type of ceramic magnet used in cabinet latches works well.

- Make certain the motor is on a flat, level surface.

Here's How:
1. Use pliers and paper clips to make two rotor cradles.
2. Use tape or rubber bands to attach the cradles to the end of the cell.
3. Attach the magnet to the upper side of the cell (glue or tape).
4. You may have to attach sticks to the side of the cell to prevent rolling.
5. Create a coil by wrapping the wire around the broomstick.

6. Slide the coil off the tube.

7. Bend out the two ends, making two coil support arms

8. Use emery or sandpaper to completely remove the varnish insulation from one arm.

9. On the other arm, remove the insulating varnish from one side of the arm only.

10. Place the rotor in the cradle and give it a flick to get the motor started.

11. You may need to adjust the coil and arms to obtain a smooth, balanced rotation.

The Science:

When electric current flows through the coil a magnetic field is generated around the copper wire. That magnetic field reacts to the field of the magnet stuck to the cell.

The fields either attract or repel, depending on the direction of the electric current.

As the coil rotates, the electric current is turned on and off as the insulated portion of the wire comes in contact with the cradle. The on/off flow of current allows the coil field to both push and pull at a different time during each rotating cycle.

Sketches & Observations:

Notes:

_____

_____

_____

_____

_____

_____

_____

HEAT-EXPANSION DEVICE

What is it? Use bits of simple hardware to demonstrate an interesting phenomenon: expansion due to heat.

What you'll need:
Checklist:
- ☐ Wood dowel rod
- ☐ Round-head screw
- ☐ Eye screw
- ☐ Candle
- ☐ Needle-nose pliers
- ☐ Screwdriver

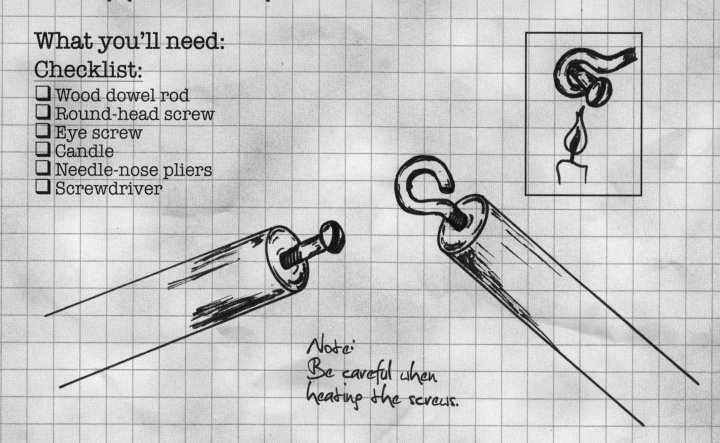

Note:
Be careful when heating the screws.

Here's How:
1. At the hardware store, select a screw eye that just fits over the head of a round-head wood screw.
2. You may need to use pliers to either squeeze the screw eye smaller or pry it open a bit. The screw eye must have a diameter very close to that of the screw head.
3. Cut two short sections of dowel rod to be used as handles.
4. Screw the screw eye into an end of one handle. Do the same for the wood screw in the other handle.
5. Check and make certain that, at room temperature, the screw head will just barely pass through the screw eye.
6. Heat the screw head in a flame.
7. Attempt to pass it through the screw eye. If the screw head has expanded sufficiently, it will not pass through.

The Science:

Common objects tend to expand and contract with temperature change. At room temperature, a solid piece of metal may appear to be motionless. A sub-microscopic look at its atoms and molecules would reveal they are in constant motion; vibrating, rotating and moving from place to place. Heat from the environment provides energy for the motion of atoms and molecules. Additional heat increases that motion. The volume occupied by the screws increases as the molecular motion increases.

What happens when you remove some of that heat by cooling the screws?

Sketches & Observations:

Notes:
_____
_____
_____
_____
_____
_____
_____
_____
_____
_____
_____
_____
_____

MAGNETIZE WITH A HAMMER

What is it? You can magnetize a nail...with a hammer!

What you'll need:
Checklist:
- ☐ Steel or iron nails, 16-penny size
- ☐ A small hammer
- ☐ A magnetic compass
- ☐ Metal paper clips

Test different materials to see if you can magnetize them with the hammer tapping method.

Here's How:
1. Use the compass to determine which direction is north.
2. Place a nail on a hard surface, such as the sidewalk, driveway, a brick, etc.
3. Point the tip of nail directly north, as indicated by the compass.
4. Tap the nail along its length about 25 to 30 times.
5. Make certain the nail keeps pointing north as you tap it.
6. Bring the nail point near the paper clips. If you have successfully magnetized the nail, you should be able to pick up several paper clips.

The Science:

Similar to the Earth itself, magnets have a north pole and a south pole. Magnetic poles are created when atoms in an object line up in a special order. Scientists call that special order magnetic domains. Some materials, like iron, readily make magnetic domains.

By pointing the nail towards the Earth's north magnetic pole and then tapping it with a hammer, the atoms of iron in the nail move about a bit, aligning themselves in the same direction as the local magnetic field. Domains are created within the nail, and it is magnetized.

Sketches & Observations:

Notes:

MAGNET TRICK

What is it? With a magnet and a pencil you can locate the part of Earth's magnetic field that passes through your house.

What you'll need:
Checklist:
☐ Circular or rectangular ceramic cabinet latch magnet
☐ Pencil
☐ Fishing line or string
☐ Fishing lure swivel

- Make several of these and see if they all point in the same direction.

← Swivel

Notes:
-Fishing line or mono-filament line works well.

Here's How:
1. It is very important that the magnet can easily rotate. Use string, line or thread that is not likely to unwind or twist.

2. Tie a fishing line swivel to the end of a length of string.

3. Use a short length of string to attach the other end of the swivel to the magnet.

4. If the magnet does not easily rotate, place a drop of oil on the swivel, or replace it.

5. Insert a pencil or dowel rod through the hole in the magnet.

6. Hang the magnet by the long string and give it a slight flick to make it spin.

7. Repeat several times.

8. You will notice that the pencil will eventually point in the same direction.

The Science:

The earth is similar to a magnet...a huge magnet with both a north and a south magnetic pole. A large portion of the earth's mantle and core is made of iron, a metal often associated with magnets.

Just as a small hand magnet has magnetic lines of force about it, the earth has the same lines of magnetic force over its surface. The free-swinging magnet on your string will align itself with the earth's nearby lines of magnetic force...even those that pass right through your house!

Sketches & Observations:

Notes:

WASHER KARATE

What is it? A spatula is used to demonstrate inertia.

What you'll need:
Checklist:
- ☐ Pancake spatula with thin blade
- ☐ Two books or blocks of wood
- ☐ Stack of heavy washers or coins

-You may want to craft some washer catchers for either side of your work area.

Stack of 10, or so, thick metal washers; pancake spatula in the process of knocking out the bottom washer.

- It may require a little practice to act upon only one washer at a time.

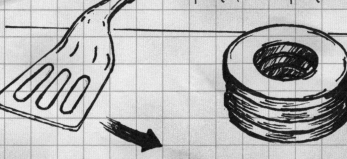

-Can you knock a washer out of the middle of the stack?

Here's How:
1. Place a stack of washers near the edge of a smooth-topped table or counter.
2. Hold the spatula blade flat against the surface.
3. With a quick flick of the wrist, slide the spatula blade towards the bottom washer in the stack.
4. The bottom washer will be ejected from the stack, and the stack will drop down without tumbling over.
5. With a back-and-forth motion, you can cause the stack to "shrink" very rapidly.

The Science:

One of the basic properties of any object is called inertia. Inertia is the resistance of an object to change its state of motion.

If the object is sitting still, it will remain so...until a force acts on it. Likewise, if an object is moving, it will keep on moving until it is acted upon.

Each washer in the stack will stay in the stack until you act on it...or push it out with the spatula. The remaining washers stay in place until something acts on them. In this case...gravity. Gravity pulls the washers down.

Sketches & Observations:

Notes:
_____
_____
_____
_____
_____
_____
_____
_____
_____
_____
_____
_____
_____

ACCELERATION OF GRAVITY DEMONSTRATOR

What is it? What does <u>accelerate</u> mean?
A metal pie pan and metal washers attached to string
are used to demonstrate acceleration of gravity.

What you'll need:
Checklist:
- ☐ String, 2 pieces,
  each approximately 1.5 m
- ☐ 20 metal hardware nuts
- ☐ Metal bucket or cake pan

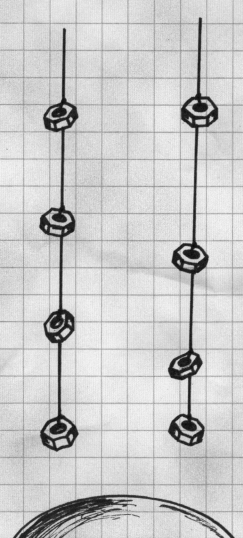

Close your eyes to make
listening to the noise a
bit easier.

What is the difference
in the noise patterns of
the falling nuts?

Here's How:
1. For the first string, use firm
   knots to attach a metal nut
   approximately every 15 cm.

2. To the second string, attach the
   nuts at the following positions
   from one end: 0 cm, 2 cm, 4 cm,
   8 cm, 13 cm, 18 cm, 24 cm, 31
   cm and 40 cm.

3. Hold the first string vertically
   over the pan with the first nut
   just touching the pan.

4. Listen carefully to the rhythm
   of the nuts as they fall against
   the metal surface.

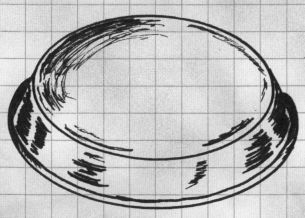

The Science:

The constant pull of gravity causes objects to fall towards the earth's center at a rate of 9.8 meters per second per second; or 9.8 m/sec^2. Simply stated, the farther an object falls towards the earth, the faster it goes. It accelerates.

As the regularly spaced nuts hit the pan, you'll notice the noise gets faster and faster...it accelerates.

The second set of nuts are spaced farther and farther apart...and if all goes well, they'll generate an even-spaced set of contact noises.

Sketches & Observations:

Notes:

_____
_____
_____
_____
_____
_____
_____
_____
_____
_____
_____
_____
_____

DISAPPEARING GLASS

What is it? You can make glass disappear before your eyes.

What you'll need:
Checklist:
- ☐ Large glass container
- ☐ Pyrex™ brand glassware
- ☐ Wesson™ brand cooking oil, or similar

To see light being refracted, put a pencil in a drinking glass filled with water. From a side view the pencil looks broken.

Use a pencil or other to break bubbles stuck to the submerged glass.

Here's How:

1. For this activity to work properly, the Pyrex™ glass must be absolutely clean. Give it a thorough washing and rinsing with soap and water. Any spotting left on the glass will create tell-tale indicators of the invisible glass.

2. The fish bowl, mixing bowl or other large glass container used to hold the oil should be clean as well. It does not need to be made of Pyrex™ glass.

3. Try to create as few bubbles as possible when pouring the oil into the large glass container. Bubbles adhering to the Pyrex™ glass will reveal its presence.

4. Fill the large container 3/4 full with oil. Allow all bubbles to rise to the surface and disperse.

5. Make careful observations as you lower a piece of Pyrex™ glass into the oil. You should not be able to see the portion of the Pyrex™ glass submerged in the oil.

6. Place a piece of common glass into the oil. It is observable when submerged.

The Science:

Scientists coined the word <u>refraction</u> to describe the bending of light as it passes from one medium to another. You probably have experienced the refraction of light reflected off of objects submerged in water. Since the index of refraction of the oil is very nearly that of Pyrex™ glass, light is not significantly refracted as it passes from the oil through the glass. Common glass has a different index of refraction than the oil and therefore is slightly visible when submerged in it. Scientists often use refraction as a method for identifying the brand or composition of unknown glass.

Sketches & Observations:

Notes:

MARSHMALLOW BLOWGUN

What is it? Use plastic pipe and fittings to make a safe blowgun that uses marshmallow ammo.

What you'll need:
Checklist:
- ☐ A bag of mini-marshmallows
- ☐ A three-foot length of half-inch PVC pipe
- ☐ Two half-inch end caps
- ☐ Two half-inch "T" fitting
- ☐ Two half-inch "elbow" fittings
- ☐ Two half-inch end caps
- ☐ PVC pipe cutter
- ☐ Two half-inch end caps

Optional:
- ☐ PVC adhesive

- Gluing the fittings together is optional.
- Occasionally wash the blowgun.
- Clean up after yourself – no stray marshmallows!
- Use only marshmallows for ammo.

Here's How:
1. Use a PVC pipe cutter or hand saw to cut pipe section in these lengths: One @ 8 inches (barrel)

                    Two @ 5 inches (handles)

                    One @ 6 inches (mouth piece)

                    Three @ 4 inches (midpoint connectors)

2. Assemble the pipe and fittings as shown.

3. Insert one mini-marshmallow into the mouthpiece pipe.

4. Aim...and blow.

The Science:

At normal temperatures, gas molecules, including air, are in constant motion. Heat from the surroundings provides the energy of motion of gas molecules.

That molecular motion is what causes gases to resist being compressed. When you blow air behind the marshmallow, the air resists being compressed and pushes the marshmallow out of the other end of the pipe.

Sketches & Observations:

Notes:

_____

_____

_____

_____

_____

_____

_____

_____

_____

HOWLING ROD

What is it? Using a simple piece of aluminum, you can generate the most incredible noises, squeals and howls.

What you'll need:
Checklist:
- ☐ Aluminum rod
- ☐ Steel wool pad
- ☐ Rosin

Optional:
- ☐ Pan of water

Ask a music teacher for some broken violin rosin.

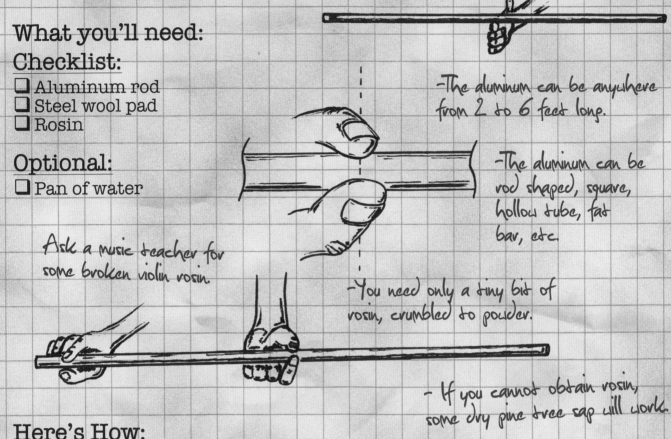

-The aluminum can be anywhere from 2 to 6 feet long.

-The aluminum can be rod shaped, square, hollow tube, fat bar, etc.

-You need only a tiny bit of rosin, crumbled to powder.

- If you cannot obtain rosin, some dry pine tree sap will work.

Here's How:
1. Obtain a solid aluminum rod from the hardware store. They are usually sold in 6-foot lengths; 1/4 or 1/2 inch in diameter.
2. Use a steel wool pad to clean all grease, oil film or surface dirt from the aluminum.
3. Find the balance point of the rod. Balance it on your index finger.
4. Tightly grip the rod at that point with your thumb and index finger only. Do not allow other fingers of that hand or your body to touch the rod.
5. Place a little rosin on your index finger and thumb of the other hand.
6. Firmly grasp the rod below the balance point and stroke it.
7. It will take some practice to master the technique of generating noise. Too much pressure from your rosin-coated fingers will muffle the vibrations. Too little pressure will not generate vibrations. It must be…"just right."

The Science:

The common sounds we hear are made of vibrations in the air...sound waves. When you stroke the aluminum rod, your skin "grabs and releases" many times. Have you ever gone down a playground slide in short pants? Slip-grab-slip-grab-slip. The same thing occurs when you properly stroke the aluminum.

The repeated slip-grab creates vibrations in the aluminum, which in turn creates vibrations in the air surrounding it.

Those vibrations travel through the air, arriving at your ears...and you detect sound. In this case, it might be an unpleasant, high-pitched sound.

Although the vibrations of the rod might be too small for you to see directly, you can see their effect. Lower the end of the vibrating rod into a pan of water. What happens?

Sketches & Observations:

Notes:

PHANTOM CRYSTALS

What is it? Common garden soil additives are used to produce invisible crystals.

What you'll need:
Checklist:
- ☐ Water-absorbing soil crystals, similar to Soil Moist™ brand
- ☐ Distilled water
- ☐ Small glass jar with lid
- ☐ Sewing needle

Optional:
- ☐ Paper clips or wire

- Hang the crystal by a thread noose. The noose appears empty when submerged.

- If you look very carefully, you can see a faint outline of the crystal.

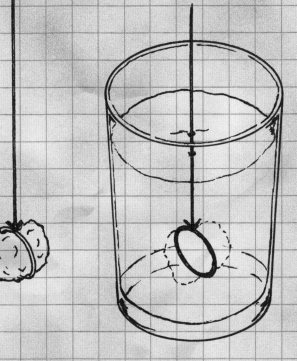

Here's How:
1. Wash and rinse a jar and lid.
2. Fill the jar 3/4 full with distilled water.
3. Select several crystals from the package and gently rinse them with a small stream of distilled water.
4. Place the cleaned crystals into the jar and allow them to sit in the water, undisturbed, for several hours.
5. The crystals will absorb water and grow to many times their original size.
6. Drain the water and refill the jar with distilled water.
7. If you notice bubbles trapped in the crystals, use a needle to pop them.
8. Make a frame to support your "invisible" crystal in the water.

The Science:

The super-absorbing crystal is a polymer (long molecule) designed by a chemist for the purpose of attracting and holding water. Most brands of such crystals are a form of methyl polyacrylate. Each molecule of MPA can attract and hold thousands of water molecules.

The water-swollen crystal is invisible in water because it is made almost entirely of water. Its index of refraction is so near that of pure water your eyes can barely detect it. Index of refraction is a measure of how much light is bent as it passes through an object.

Sketches & Observations:

Notes:

_____

_____

_____

_____

_____

_____

_____

_____

_____

_____

_____

_____

_____

TRICK YOUR OWN EYES!

What is it? The pattern on a spinning wheel creates an incredible optical illusion...the skin is twisting off of your hand! Ugggh!

What you'll need:
Checklist:

- ☐ 6"-diameter lawnmower wheel or similar
- ☐ Nut and bolt to be used as an axle
- ☐ 6"-diameter paper or cardboard disc
- ☐ Black marker
- ☐ Red marker
- ☐ Tape or glue

Hint
-Don't spin the wheel too fast.

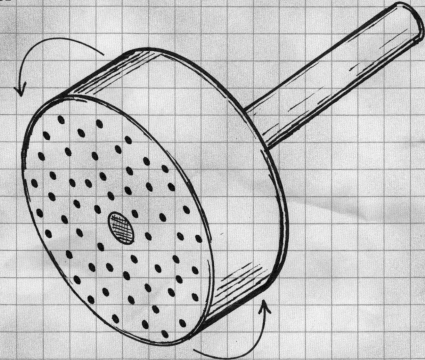

-Stare at a waterfall for a while and then look at something nearby. It may, for an instant, look like it is moving upwards.

Here's How:

1. Fasten a bolt through the wheel center and secure with a nut.
2. Select a bolt that is long enough to provide a handle on the back side of the wheel.
3. Use a dark marker to make 50 or 60 small dots on the cardboard disk.
4. Place one large red dot at the center of the disc.
5. Use tape or glue to attach the disc to the wheel.
6. While staring at the red dot, spin the wheel slowly...so just the outer dots blur.
7. After staring at the red dot for fifteen seconds, look at the lines in the palm of your hand. Your skin is twisting!

The Science:

It is the nature of your eyes and brain to detect motion and get used to a regular moving pattern. When you then suddenly look at something standing still, your eyes see movement in the opposite direction. Scientists call this phenomenon the waterfall effect. It is caused by the rate nerve impulses in your brain change, slowing a bit when they are repeated in one direction. When that repetition quickly stops, opposing impulses begin to fire, and for a short time the brain is tricked into thinking the pulses are traveling in the opposite direction.

Sketches & Observations:

Notes:

_____
_____
_____
_____
_____
_____
_____
_____
_____
_____
_____
_____

LEAF BLOWER PHYSICS

What is it? You can use a leaf blower to perform some fantastic physics activities...make an entire roll of TP airborne...create the most impossible beach ball-balancing effect ever!

What you'll need:
Checklist:
- [ ] A leaf blower
- [ ] Extension cord
- [ ] Safety glasses
- [ ] Roll of toilet tissue
- [ ] Stick or dowel rod
- [ ] Empty two-liter soda bottle or Playball

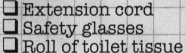
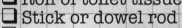
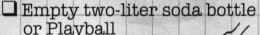
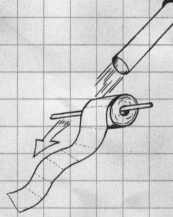

Note:
-Always wear eye protection.
Hint:
-Try a lightweight Playball instead of a bottle.

Here's How:

1. Fill an empty two-liter soda bottle with hot water to assist in removing the label, glue and any attachments.

2. Empty the bottle but leave 2 or 3 inches of water in the bottle.

3. Seal the cap.

4. Remove all attachments from the leaf blower.

5. Point the blower up and place the bottle in the air stream. The stream should support the bottle.

6. Slowly tilt the stream to about 45 degrees. What happens to the bottle? You can use a Playball instead of a bottle.

7. For a dramatic effect, shoot the air stream over the top of a roll of toilet paper, which can turn on a stick or dowel.

The Science:

   The bottle (or ball) is supported in the vertical air stream because there is a sufficient number of high-speed air molecules striking the lower side of the ball to overcome the downward pull of gravity. As the stream of air is tilted a bit, the ball begins to fall...but hovers about halfway out of the stream. It remains there, and it does not shoot away. As the ball falls, the stream rushes over the top of the ball, lowering air pressure on the upper surface. There remains enough normal air pressure under the ball to support it. The same phenomenon occurs on the sides of the ball as well...high pressure on one side and lower pressure on the other.

Sketches & Observations:

Notes:

_____
_____
_____
_____
_____
_____
_____
_____
_____
_____
_____
_____
_____

MAGIC FUNNEL TRICK

What is it? So simple yet so impossible...you
can not blow a ping pong ball out of a funnel.

What you'll need:
Checklist:
- ☐ Small funnel
- ☐ Ping pong ball

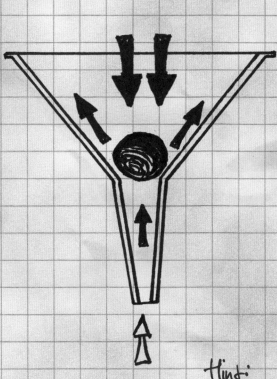

Hint:
-Keep the funnel clean.

Here's How:
1. Put a ping pong ball into the funnel bowl.
2. Tip your head back and try to blow the ball out of the funnel.

The Science:

We live at the bottom of an ocean of air. The air around us exerts a great deal of pressure; about 15 pounds on every square inch. A bowling ball weighs about that amount. So, you can imagine that there is a "bowling ball" pushing down on every square inch of objects on the earth's surface.

When air rushes sideways on the surface of the ping pong ball, the pressure it exerts is lowered a bit. That means the atmospheric pressure pushing on the top is exerting a bit more force...than you can overcome with your breath.

Sketches & Observations:

Notes:
_____
_____
_____
_____
_____
_____
_____
_____
_____
_____
_____
_____

SPEAKING TUBES

What is it? Use a garden hose and funnels to transmit secret messages.

Note:
You can attach several lengths of hose. Messages can be sent more than 100 feet through a garden hose.

What you'll need:
Checklist:
☐ Two small plastic funnels
☐ Garden hose
☐ Duct tape

— Occasionally wash the funnels with soap and water.

Here's How:
1. Obtain two plastic funnels, about 4" in diameter or larger.
2. Use a saw or shop knife to remove the narrow end of the funnel, leaving a cone.
3. The small end of the funnel should be cut to leave a hole that will just fit over the end of the hose.
4. Use duct tape to attach a modified funnel to each end of the hose.
5. Unroll the hose and practice speaking and listening at the ends of the funnel.

The Science:

A speaking tube or voicepipe is a device based around two cones connected by an air pipe through which speech can be transmitted over an extended distance. While its most common use was in intra-ship communications, the principle was also used in fine homes and offices of the 19th century, as well as fine automobiles, military aircraft and even locomotives. For most purposes, the device was outmoded by the telephone and its widespread adoption.

Sketches & Observations:

Notes:

_____
_____
_____
_____
_____
_____
_____
_____
_____
_____
_____
_____

RATTLESNAKE EGGS

What is it? This is a classic science-based practical joke.
It will scare everyone!

What you'll need:
Checklist:

- ☐ Wire coat hanger or large paper clip
- ☐ Small rubber bands
- ☐ Small metal bolt washer or button
- ☐ Envelope
- ☐ Pliers with wire cutter
- ☐ Small metal file

Hint:
-Decorate the envelope with scientific messages such as <u>fragile</u>, <u>keep at warm temperatures</u>, <u>biological specimen</u> or <u>keep from direct sunlight</u>.

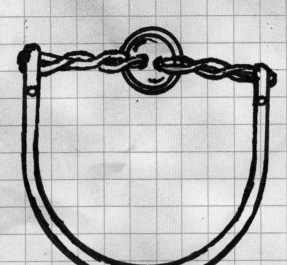

Here's How:

1. Use wire cutters to remove a U-shaped piece from the hook of a wire coat hanger.
2. Use a file or sandpaper to smooth the ends of the "U."
3. Attach two small rubber bands to a metal bolt washer.
4. Attach the other side of the rubber bands to the two U-arms.
5. Use pliers to fold the wire ends over to capture the rubber bands.
6. Wind up the washer.
7. Carefully slide the device into a "danger"-decorated envelope. Do not allow the washer to unwind.
8. Do not seal the envelope.
9. Place the envelope is a location where your unsuspecting victim will see it.

The Science:

Scientists who study human behavior often observe a person's "response" to a "stimulus." This activity provides the opportunity to see the physiology of a couple of common human reactions: the startle reflex (from the buzzing sound) and the tickle reflex (from the vibrations felt). Both are responses to unexpected stimulations of sound and motion coming from the envelope.

Observe your "victim" and see if they follow these common responses to the scary envelope stimulus:

1. Do they quickly move away from the stimulus?
2. Does their breathing rate increase?
3. Do both their arms and legs contract at the same time?
4. Do their eyes start and continue to blink?

Sketches & Observations:

Notes:

_____
_____
_____
_____
_____
_____
_____
_____
_____
_____
_____
_____

MAGIC WAND

What is it? With the help of a bit of static electricity, a plastic pipe is converted to a magic wand.

What you'll need:
Checklist:
- ☐ A long piece of lumber, 1x4, 2x4, etc.
- ☐ Soup ladle or ice cream scoop
- ☐ Lubricating oil
- ☐ 1/2-inch PVC pipe, 2 to 3 feet long
- ☐ Piece of wool cloth, glove or sock

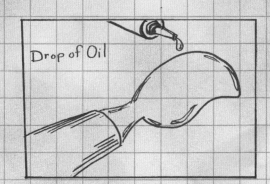

Drop of Oil

-This activity works best when the air is dry. Humid air helps the static charge to leak away.

-You can use an inflated balloon instead of the plastic rod.

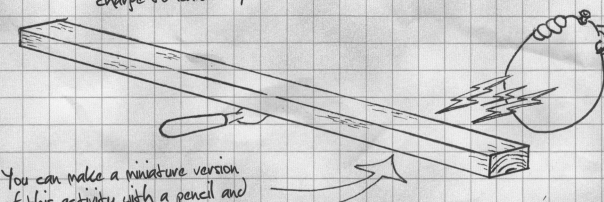

You can make a miniature version of this activity with a pencil and a charged hair comb.

Here's How:
1. Invert the scoop or spoon on a flat level surface.
2. Place only one or two drops of oil at the center of the pivot point.
3. Balance the stick or board on the pivot point.
4. The oil should allow the stick to freely rotate.
5. Place a static charge on the plastic "wand" by stroking it against the wool cloth repeatedly, in one direction only!
6. Hold the charged wand near the end of the stick. Do not touch the stick with the wand.

The Science:

The action of stroking the cloth caused some of the loosely attached electrons on it to be dislodged and deposited on the rod. If you hold the charged rod (or balloon) near the cloth, you might hear the snap of miniature lightning bolts as the electrons jump back to the cloth.

The electrons deposited on the rod give the rod a negative charge. Although the stick has no charge, it is relatively positive, compared to the negative charge on the rod. That difference in charge is sufficient to create an attraction that moves the stick.

Sketches & Observations:

Notes:
_____
_____
_____
_____
_____
_____
_____
_____
_____
_____
_____
_____
_____
_____

WORMERY

What is it? <u>Build a hotel for some squirmy friends.</u>
They will entertain and educate as you observe their life habits.

What you'll need:
Checklist:
- ☐ Several earthworms, from a bait shop or your back yard
- ☐ A large glass jar or two panes of glass and some 1x2 lumber
- ☐ Duct tape
- ☐ Large cloth, rag or heavy paper bag
- ☐ Potting soil
- ☐ Non-instant coffee grounds
- ☐ Lettuce
- ☐ Leaves and grass

Notes:
- A good time to dig for worms is after it rains, or soak the yard with a hose.
- Store your wormery covered, or in a dark place.
- If the wormery walls get steamy, you've added too much water.

Hint:
You can use a tall jar as a substitute. Leave lid off or poke air holes in it.

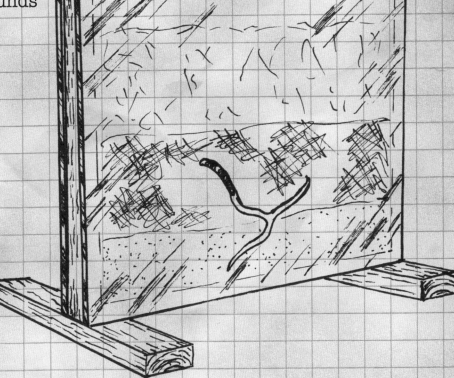

Here's How:

1. Use the lumber and glass panes to fabricate a thin aquarium-like structure.

2. Leave the top open.

3. Use duct tape to attach the glass to the lumber.

4. Cover all sharp edges with tape.

5. Fill the cavity with loose soil...do not compact it.

6. Slightly moisten the soil...but not too much water!

7. Place your worms on the soil and cover them with a thin layer of grass and crumbled leaves.

8. Create a dark habitat...cover the wormery with a cloth or paper bag. Worms prefer darkness.

9. After a couple of days, remove the cover and observe the action of the worms.

10. To feed them, lay some fresh shredded lettuce and a few coffee grounds on the surface.

11. After observing the worms for a couple of weeks, release them back into your yard.

The Science:

Worms live underground, and that makes it challenging to observe what they're doing. The wormery allows you to monitor their movements.

Earthworms are from a group of animals called invertebrates. They have no bones or skeleton. They move about using muscles to lengthen themselves and then pull their bottom end toward their head.

When worms tunnel through soil, they are actually eating it. The soil meal goes in one end of the worm and out the other. By creating tunnels, the worms break up the soil and make it easier for water to reach plant roots. Worms also break down dead and rotten plant material, which adds nutrients to the soil.

Sketches & Observations:

Notes:

_____
_____
_____
_____
_____
_____
_____
_____
_____
_____

AIR CANNON

What is it? Use a bucket to create a device that shoots an air cannonball vortex up to 100 feet.

What you'll need:
Checklist:
- ☐ A five-gallon bucket or small plastic trash can
- ☐ Rubber sheet (shower curtain, tarp, etc)
- ☐ Large hose clamp(s) or string and duct tape
- ☐ Saw or cutting blade
- ☐ Mallet or large dowel

Notes:
- A piece of old shower curtain or several layers of plastic trash bags will work.
- If you use a dowel rod as a beater, sand the end edges to round them over a bit.

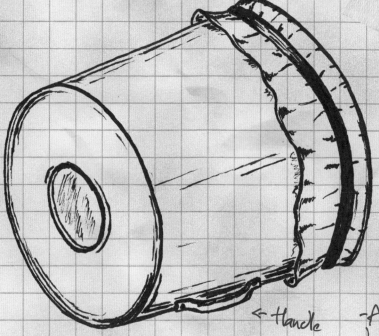

← Handle

-Try using the air cannon to blow out a candle at a distance...even from another room

-Add a little smoke to the drum to make the air cannonball visible; incense works well

Here's How:
1. Cut a four-inch-diameter hole in the center of the bucket bottom.
2. Stretch a sheet of rubber over the open end of the bucket.
3. Secure the sheet taut to the rim of the bucket with tape and string, or a large hose clamp.
4. Strike the rubber with a drum mallet or dowel rod.
5. A ring of air will travel with force across the room.

The Science:

This activity demonstrates that air occupies space. As the rubber sheet is pushed into the bucket, the interior volume decreases, and for a moment the air pressure increases. That increase in pressure forces some of the air out through the hole. The velocity at which the air leaves the hole is inversely proportional to the diameter of the hole: The smaller the hole, the faster it leaves.

The proper name for the device is "vortex generator." The "cannonball" of air is actually a doughnut-shaped (toroid) pulse of air. Such a shape is generated because air exiting the bucket at the center of the hole is traveling a bit faster than the air exiting at the edge of the hole, where it is slowed a bit when it rubs against the bucket.

Sketches & Observations:

Notes:

_____
_____
_____
_____
_____
_____
_____
_____
_____
_____
_____
_____
_____
_____

Thinking Like a Scientist

Scientists in all fields of study use the same set of skills to perform their work. You will find that chemists, biologists, physicists, astronomers and geologists are experts at "science process skills."

Each of the activities in this book includes at least one of those skills. As you perform an activity, you will be practicing the use of that skill, making you a better scientist.

Here is a short list of some science process skills and suggestions on how to practice them:

Data recording and analysis: Keep good and timely notes while you work on a science project. Make note of both successes and failures. With practice, you will be able to ponder your notes and perhaps find the causes of problems, or find better methods of performing the activity.

Measurement: Practice using all sorts of devices to take measurements: rulers, yardsticks, thermometers, scales and balances, etc. Don't just guess. Measure it!

Observation: Use your eyes and your brain to thoughtfully gather information about an object or event. Scientists do not merely "look" at an object; they observe it, making mental notes of what they observe.

Prediction: Scientists rarely just guess. More often, they predict. A prediction is a guess based on past experience. Scientists stop and think before they speak or make a guess.

Experimenting and testing: Scientists do not throw things together to see what happens. They experiment by testing one thing at a time, while they keep everything else constant, or the same.

Calculating: All scientists are capable of performing a variety of mathematical functions. It's OK to use a calculator, but you should practice calculating on your own from time to time.

Manipulating materials and equipment: Most scientists are "hands-on" types of folks. They constantly get trained or train themselves to use all sorts of tools, materials and equipment. Practice. Practice. Practice. Doing so will allow you to be a master science equipment operator.

Adapting: Scientists have the ability to change to the situation, while staying focused on an original objective. They respond well to "Oooops, that wasn't supposed to happen." And scientists will often say, "Let's try it again."

Precision and accuracy: Scientists are careful. They tend to details and specifics in all aspects of an activity. They watch what they are doing.

Wizard IV's Calendar of Meteor Showers

Month	Approx. Week	Shower Name	Specs
January	1st Week	Quadrantids	Lasts an hour, 40 blue meteors per hour, very fast (25 miles/sec.)
April	3rd Week	Lyrids	Lyrids meteors explode and often leave dust trains.
May	1st Week	Eta Aquarids	Very rarely observed, these falling stars are remnants of Halley's comet.
June	End of 2nd Week	Lyrids	Small meteors, about 10 per hour
July	End of 4th Week	Delta Aquarids	Yellow meteors, about 20 per hour
July	End of 4th Week	Capricornids	15 per hour, yellow and very bright, occasional fireball
August	2nd Week	Perseids	60 meteors per hour
October	End of 1st Week	Draconids	10 meteors per hour in a very dark sky
October	End of 3rd Week	Orionids	20 very fast green or yellow meteors per hour, some fireballs
November	Middle of 3rd Week	Leonids	Up to 100 per hour
December	End of 2nd Week	Geminids	Very reliable shower; white, yellow, blue, green and red meteors.

The above listed dates are approximate. You should check for the specific times and dates for your area.

A piece of sand or rock moving through space is called a METEOROID.

The visible path of a meteoroid in our atmosphere is called a METEOR.

If it strikes the earth, it is called a METEORITE.

Wizard IV's
METRIC SYSTEM
Rules of Thumb

A dime is about one **millimeter** thick.

A small metal paper clip weighs about one **gram**.

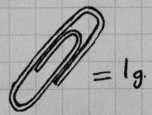

A shirt button is about one **centimeter** in diameter.

Three cans of soda contain together about a **liter** of liquid.

A washing machine is about one **meter** tall.

Index

About the Wizards

Nearly 210 years ago, the son of a poor blacksmith read a book he was repairing while performing his duties as an apprentice in a bookbinder's shop. This book captured the imagination of the young teenager, Michael Faraday. He delighted in learning of recent discoveries in the fledgling field of science. That scientific interest led him to a position at the Royal Institution of Great Britain, where Faraday made many great scientific discoveries of his own, one of which changed our world forever. However, he is most renowned for his ability to communicate science to the public.

Michael Faraday was indeed a masterful science communicator. Queen Victoria called him "Wizard; a man who caused us to experience the truest beauty of the Creation."

Other science communicators have answered the call to be providers of common sense and understanding of scientific innovations. At the end of World War II, the term "atomic energy" entered the public lexicon, leaving most of the public fearful and apprehensive of anything tagged "nuclear." Dr. Hubert Alyea at Princeton was engaged by the United Nations to visit 88 countries, explaining the nature and positive possibilities of atomic energy to millions of people in attentive audiences. Often compared to Faraday, Dr. Alyea took the role of Wizard II, and served as the key inspiration for the Disney movie *The Absent-Minded Professor*.

In the 1950's, when the Sputnik satellite began the space race and subsequent pursuit of science learning, the public turned to yet another renowned science communicator, Don Herbert, better known as television's Mr. Wizard. For five decades, generations of youngsters were inspired to learn the "science of everyday living" from the third great Wizard.

The current holder of the Wizard title – Steven Jacobs (Wizard IV) – was mentored by two of those famed science communicators. Alyea taught him chemistry and the art of being a scientific raconteur. Mr. Wizard trained him to follow in his footsteps in television. In 1995, at the Royal Institution of Great Britain, near the memorial of Wizard I, Michael Faraday, the torch was passed. Wizard IV was given the challenge of carrying the science communicator's "light of illumination."

Perhaps you can be Wizard Five!